Wallace is a friendly dog.
He is always hungry.

Wherever Gabe is, Wallace is always there.

Wallace
the
Hungry Dog

By
Roger Priddy

Gabe, Teddy and Wallace are best friends.

If Gabe is in the bath,

Wallace gets in too!

Gabe and Wallace love the park.

Today they are playing on
the swings...

...and splashing in the mud!

But all this exercise makes
Wallace very hungry.

Wallace loves food more than anything else.

He looks for something to
eat wherever he is.

He even chases after
people if they have food!

"Naughty dog!"

He eats the fruit that Dad is growing.

"Wallace! No!"

And even the rotten apples that fall off the tree.

**Then he has a
tummy ache…**

...and is sick. This gets
him into big trouble!

Gabe thinks that if Wallace is full then he won't eat bad things.

So he decides to feed him more dog food!

But Wallace just eats everything he is given.

And ends up very fat.

Now Wallace can't chase people in the park...

...or play fun games
with Gabe and Teddy.

Gabe is sad. He hadn't meant to make Wallace fat.

So he takes him to the vet, who says, "Less food and more exercise."

Gabe sets about getting Wallace fit again.

They go for a run...

...a cycle ride,

and a swim!

At last the three friends are having fun again!

Wallace is a healthier dog ... but he still dreams about food!